crab

crab

•   •   •   •

drip

drip

• • • •

frog

frog

. . . .

brush

brush

· · · —

dress

dress

. . . —

train

train

• • — •

sleep

sleep

• • • — •

fright

fright

· · —— ·

broom

broom

. . . — .

growl

growl

We like to skip,
clap and bang
a drum.

I can pick
some plums.

Come to the
sports track!

Have you ever been on a train?